Schott New York

Gregory Spears
b.1977

Toccata
(Troika)
for solo piano

Full score

ED 30285

SCHOTT

Mainz · London · Madrid · New York · Paris · Prague · Tokyo · Toronto
© 2018 Schott Helicon Music Corporation, New York · Printed in USA

Commissioned by The Stecher and Horowitz Foundation for the
2018 New York International Piano Competition

Performance Notes

Troika is a Russian word meaning "set of three" or a "sled pulled by three horses." In many places in the score there are three rhythmic layers working at different speeds to create a sense of forward motion. Sometimes these layers create a sense of a headlong rush, at other points the music glides along gently. The pianist may find places in the score that evoke other aspects of a troika ride: the winter wind, snow flurries, sleigh bells, horses galloping in tandem, bumps in the path, stars, or perhaps even a moonrise. The work is in three sections with a final coda that repeats material from the opening.

Pedaling guidelines are included at various points in the piece. Performers may wish to nuance these in order to fit their individual interpretation.

Duration

ca. 9 minutes

TOCCATA
(Troika)

Gregory Spears (2018)

* Keep a steady pulse throughout.

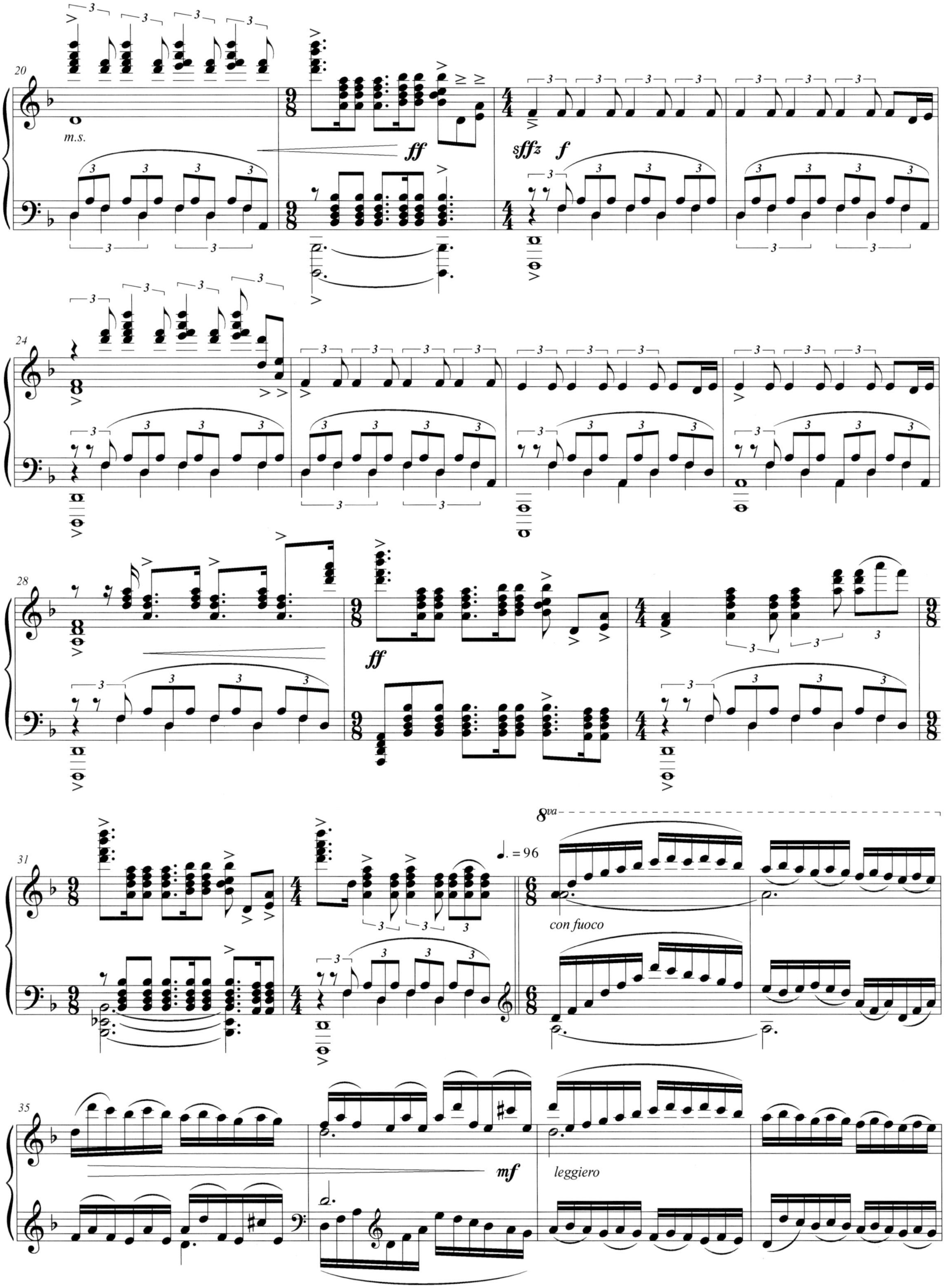
20
m.s.
ff
sffz f
24
28
ff
31
♩. = 96
8va
con fuoco
35
mf
leggiero

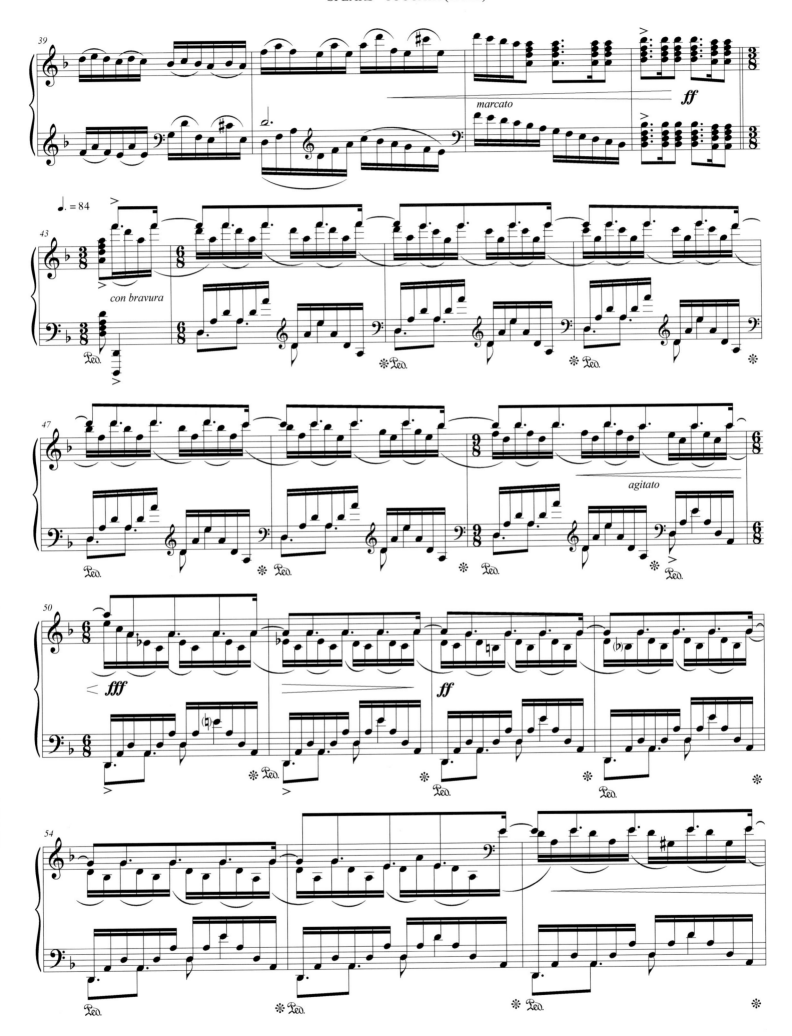

* All accents in this section should be bell-like
  and resonate through the texture.

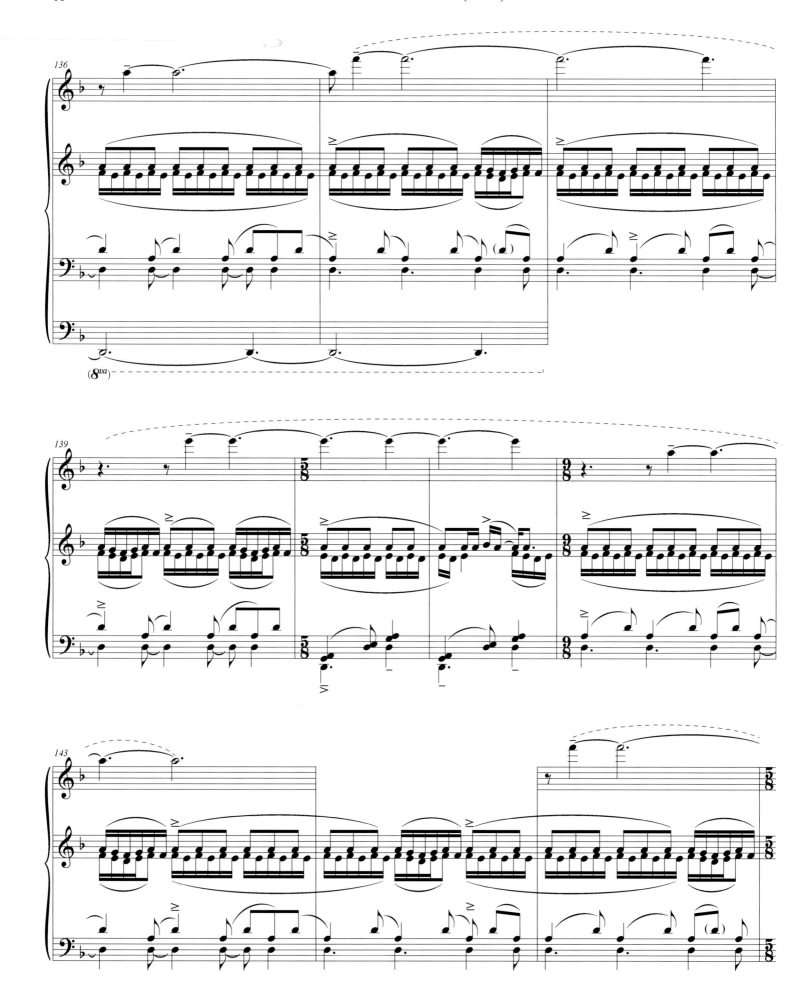

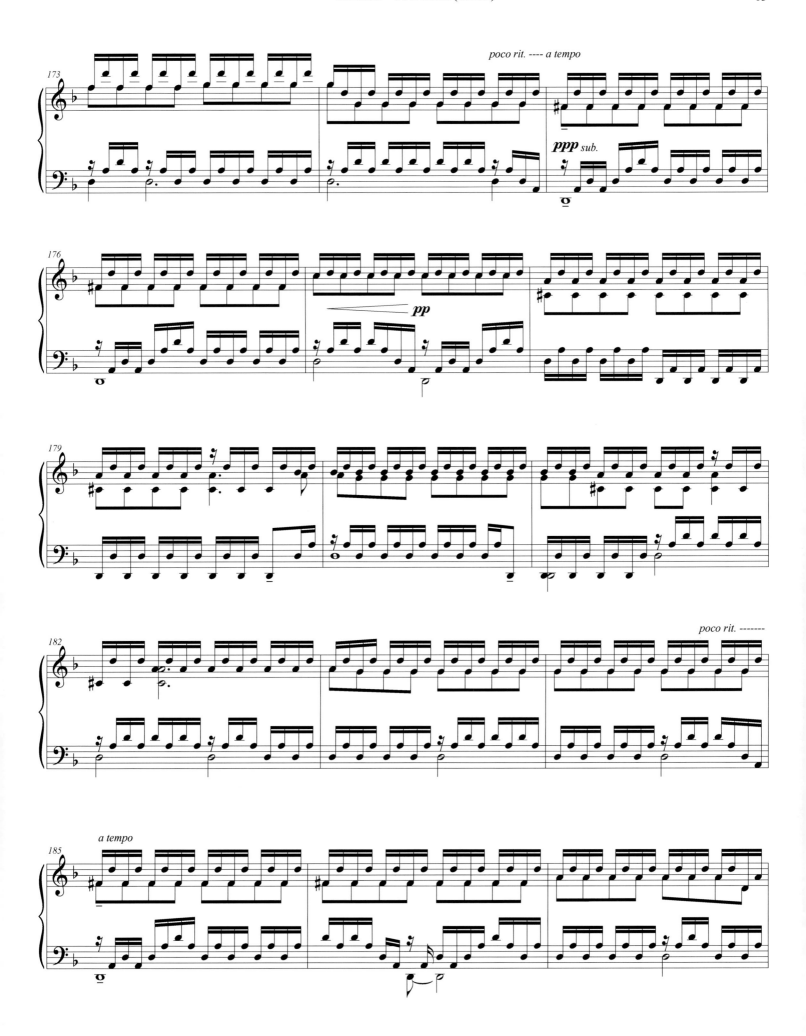

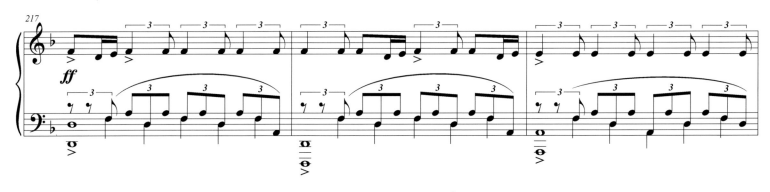

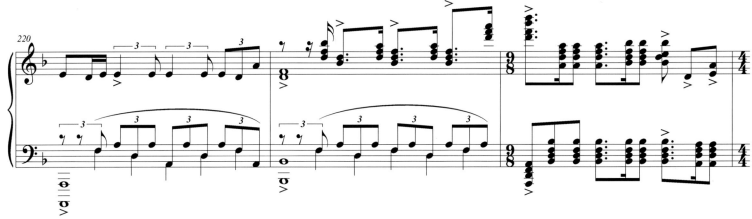

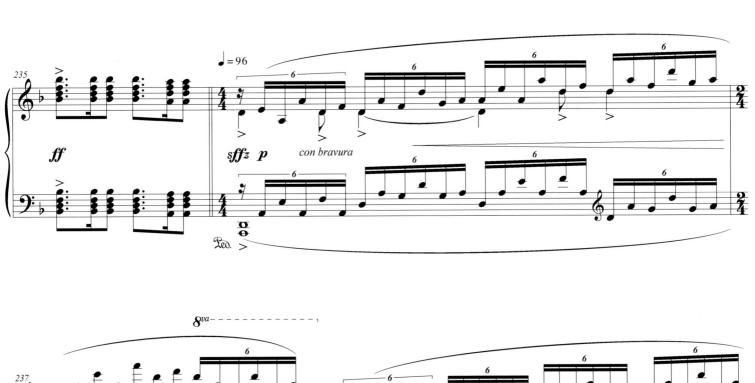

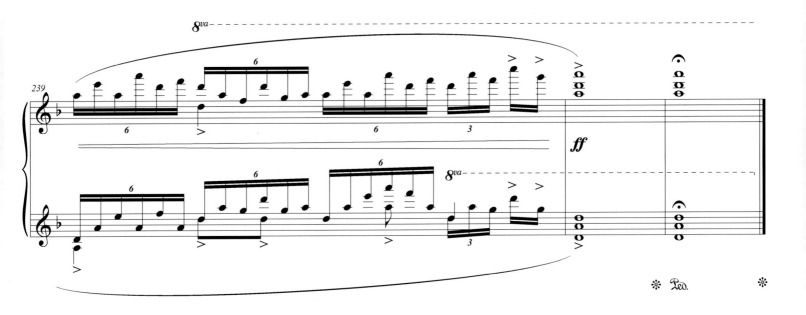